Ben Bat Is Sad

by Liza Charlesworth

ISBN: 978-1-338-84428-3

Art Director: Tannaz Fassihi; Designer: Cynthia Ng; Illustrated by Kevin Zimmer
Copyright © Liza Charlesworth. All rights reserved. Published by Scholastic Inc.

3 4 5 6 7 68 26 25 24

Printed in Jiaxing, China. First printing, June 2022.

Ben Bat is sad.
Sob, sob, sob!
"I want a pal!" said Ben.

Ben Bat met a cat.
"Can I be your pal?" said Ben.
But the cat ran.

Ben Bat met a pug.
"Can I be your pal?" said Ben.
But the pug ran.

Ben Bat met a man.
"Can I be your pal?" said Ben.
But the man ran.

Sob, sob, sob.
"I want a pal!" said Ben.

Ben Bat met a big bug.
Sob, sob, sob.
"I want a pal!" it said.
The big bug was as sad as Ben!

The big bug had
a lot of spots!
It had six legs!

8

But Ben Bat did NOT run.
Ben said, "Can I be your pal?"
"YES!" said the big bug.

Ben Bat and the big bug had a lot of fun.

Zip, zip!

Hop, hop!

Sit, sit!

Nap, nap!

Hug, hug!
Ben Bat is NOT sad.
Ben Bat has a pal!

13

Read & Review

Invite your learner to point to each short-vowel word and read it aloud.

Short a

ran
nap
cat
bat
had
sad
man
pal
and
can
has
as
am

Short e

Ben   legs
met   yes

Short o

lot
hop
not
sob
spots

Short i

it big
did
sit is
zip six

Short u

bug
pug
but
run
fun hug

15

Fun Fill-Ins

Read the sentences aloud, inviting your learner to complete them using the short-vowel words in the box.

> fun   big   Ben   ran   not

1. The name of the bat is _____.

2. The cat, pug, and man all _____.

3. Ben met a bug that was _____.

4. Did the big bug run?
   He did _____!

5. Ben Bat and the
   big bug had a lot of _____.